A LITTLE BOOK OF
·NURSERY·
RHYMES

ILLUSTRATED BY
DENYSE STEPHEN

AWARD PUBLICATIONS LIMITED

ISBN 0-86163-383-0

Copyright © 1987 Templar Publishing

First published 1987 by Century Hutchinson Children's Books

This edition published 1989 by Award Publications Limited,
Spring House, Spring Place, Kentish Town, London NW5 3BH

Printed in Malaysia

INTRODUCTION

Our best-loved nursery rhymes date back hundreds of years. Some were composed especially for children, others are colourful adaptations of old ballads, streetcries, proverbs and prayers. Together, they remain many of our earliest and happiest memories. This charmingly illustrated collection is a lively mixture of favourite rhymes and traditional riddles, which will entertain children – and parents – everywhere.

THE GRAND OLD DUKE OF YORK

Oh, the grand old Duke of York,
He had ten thousand men;
He marched them up to the top of a hill,
And he marched them down again.
And when they were up, they were up,
And when they were down, they were down,
And when they were only half way up,
They were neither up nor down.

· RIDDLE ·

In marble halls as white as milk,
Lined with a skin as soft as silk,
Within a fountain crystal-clear,
A golden apple doth appear.
No doors there are to this stronghold,
Yet thieves break in and steal the gold.

(An egg)

LITTLE BO-PEEP

Little Bo-Peep has lost her sheep,
And doesn't know where to find them;
Leave them alone, and they'll come home,
Bringing their tails behind them.

MARY, MARY, QUITE CONTRARY

Mary, Mary, quite contrary,
How does your garden grow?
With silver bells and cockle shells,
And pretty maids all in a row.

I ASKED MY MOTHER

I asked my mother for fifty cents
To see the elephant jump the fence.
He jumped so high that he touched the sky
And never came back till the Fourth of July.

THIS LITTLE PIG WENT TO MARKET

This little pig went to market,
This little pig stayed at home,
This little pig had roast beef,
This little pig had none,
And this little pig cried, Wee, wee, wee,
All the way home.

• RIDDLE •

A riddle, a riddle, as I suppose,
A hundred eyes, and never a nose.

(A potato)

BAA, BAA, BLACK SHEEP

Baa, baa, black sheep,
Have you any wool?
Yes, sir, yes, sir,
Three bags full;
One for the master,
And one for the dame,
And one for the little boy
Who lives down the lane.

RING-A-RING O'ROSES

Ring-a-ring o'roses,
A pocket full of posies,
A-tishoo! A-tishoo!
We all fall down.

HICKETY PICKETY, MY BLACK HEN

Hickety Pickety, my black hen,
She lays eggs for gentlemen;
Sometimes nine, and sometimes ten,
Hickety Pickety, my black hen.

LITTLE MISS MUFFET

Little Miss Muffet,
Sat on a tuffet,
Eating her curds and whey.
Along came a spider,
Who sat down beside her,
And frightened Miss Muffet away.

HICKORY, DICKORY, DOCK

Hickory, dickory, dock,
The mouse ran up the clock.
The clock struck one,
The mouse ran down,
Hickory, dickory, dock.

SOLOMON GRUNDY

Solomon Grundy,
Born on a Monday,
Christened on Tuesday,
Married on Wednesday,
Took ill on Thursday,
Worse on Friday,
Died on Saturday,
Buried on Sunday,
This is the end
Of Solomon Grundy.

THE QUEEN OF HEARTS

The Queen of Hearts
She made some tarts,
All on a summer's day;
The Knave of Hearts
He stole the tarts,
And took them clean away.

The King of Hearts
Called for the tarts,
And beat the Knave full sore;
The Knave of Hearts
Brought back the tarts,
And vowed he'd steal no more.

HEY DIDDLE, DIDDLE

Hey diddle, diddle,
The cat and the fiddle,
The cow jumped over the moon;
The little dog laughed
To see such fun,
And the dish ran away with the spoon.

JACK AND JILL

Jack and Jill went up the hill
To fetch a pail of water;
Jack fell down and broke his crown
And Jill came tumbling after.

Up Jack got and home did trot
As fast as he could caper;
Went to bed and bound his head
With vinegar and brown paper.

When Jill came in how she did grin
To see Jack's paper plaster;
Mother vexed, did whip her next
For causing Jack's disaster.

Little Nancy Etticoat with a white petticoat,
And a red nose;
The longer she stands, the shorter she grows.

(A candle)

OLD KING COLE

Old King Cole
Was a merry old soul,
And merry old soul was he;
He called for his pipe,
And he called for his bowl,
And he called for his fiddlers three.

Every fiddler he had a fiddle,
And a very fine fiddle had he;
Oh, there's none so rare,
As can compare
With King Cole and his fiddlers three.

RIDE A COCK-HORSE

Ride a cock-horse to Banbury Cross,
To see a fine lady upon a white horse;
With rings on her fingers and bells on her toes,
She shall have music wherever she goes.

• RIDDLE •

I've seen you where you never were,
And where you ne'er will be,
And yet you in that very same place,
May still be seen by me.

(Mirror reflection)

MARY HAD A LITTLE LAMB

Mary had a little lamb,
Its fleece was white as snow;
And everywhere that Mary went
The lamb was sure to go.

It followed her to school one day,
That was against the rule;
It made the children laugh and play
To see a lamb at school.

And so the teacher turned it out,
But still it lingered near;
And waited patiently about
Till Mary did appear.

"Why does the lamb love Mary so?"
The eager children cry.
"Why, Mary loves the lamb, you know,"
The teacher did reply.

HUMPTY DUMPTY

Humpty Dumpty sat on a wall,
Humpty Dumpty had a geat fall;
All the King's horses and all the King's men
Couldn't put Humpty together again.

TWO CATS OF KILKENNY

There were two cats of Kilkenny,
Each thought there were one cat too many;
So they fought and they fit,
And they scratched and they bit,
Till, excepting their nails
And the tips of their tails,
Instead of two cats, there weren't any.

· RIDDLE ·

I have a little sister, they call her Peep, Peep;
She wades the waters, deep, deep, deep;
She climbs the mountains high, high, high;
Poor little creature, she has but one eye!

(A star)

Heyhow for Hallowe'en
When all the witches are to be seen,
Some in black and some in green,
Heyhow for Hallowe'en.

• RIDDLE •

Thirty white horses upon a red hill,
Now they tramp, now they champ,
Now they stand still.

(Teeth and gums)

BOYS AND GIRLS

Boys and girls come out to play,
The moon doth shine as bright as day,
Leave your supper, and leave your sleep,
And come with your playfellows into the street.
Come with a whoop, come with a call,
Come with a good will, or come not at all.
Up the ladder and down the wall,
A halfpenny loaf will serve us all.
You find milk, and I'll find flour,
And we'll have a pudding in half an hour.

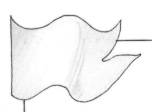

I SAW A SHIP A-SAILING

I saw a ship a-sailing,
A-sailing on the sea,
And oh but it was laden
With pretty things for me.

There were comfits in the cabin,
And sweetmeats in the hold;
The sails were made of silk,
And the masts were all of gold.

The four-and-twenty sailors,
That stood between the decks,
Were four-and-twenty white mice
With chains about their necks.

The captain was a duck
With a jacket on his back,
And when the ship began to move
The captain said Quack! Quack!

SING A SONG OF SIXPENCE

Sing a song of sixpence,
A pocket full of rye;
Four and twenty blackbirds
Baked in a pie.

When the pie was opened
The birds began to sing;
Was not that a dainty dish
To set before the king?

The king was in his counting house
Counting out his money;
The queen was in the parlour
Eating bread and honey.

The maid was in the garden
Hanging out the clothes;
There came a little blackbird,
And snapped off her nose.

THE MULBERRY BUSH

Here we go round the mulberry bush,
The mulberry bush, the mulberry bush,
Here we go round the mulberry bush,
On a cold and frosty morning.

This is the way we clap our hands,
Clap our hands, clap our hands,
This is the way we clap our hands,
On a cold and frosty morning.

I'M GLAD

I'm glad the sky is painted blue,
And the earth is painted green,
With such a lot of nice fresh air
All sandwiched in between.

HUSH-A-BYE BABY

Hush-a-bye, baby, on the tree top,
When the wind blows, the cradle will rock;
When the bough breaks, the cradle will fall,
Down will come baby, cradle and all.